Piano
Initial

Pieces & Exercises
for Trinity College London exams

2015-2017

Published by
Trinity College London
www.trinitycollege.com

Registered in the UK
Company no. 02683033
Charity no. 1014792

Printed in Great Britain by Caligraving Ltd.

Gavotte

(optional duet part)

Arr. Carol Barratt

James Hook
(1746-1827)

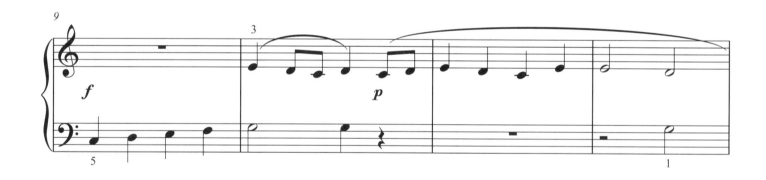

Gavotte

(candidate solo part)

Arr. Carol Barratt

James Hook
(1746-1827)

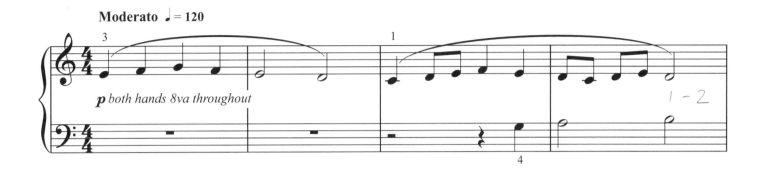

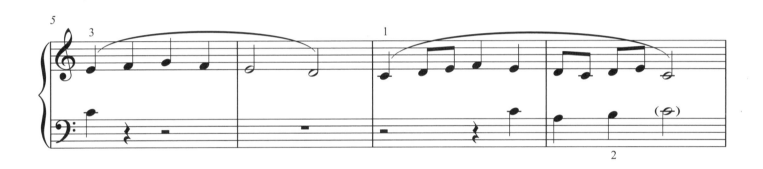

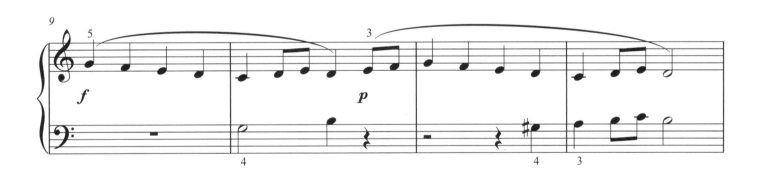

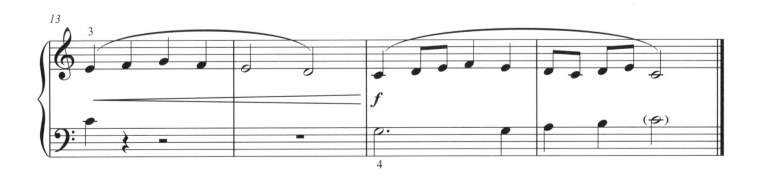

Summer Swing

Ed. Peter Wild

August Eberhard Müller
(1767-1817)

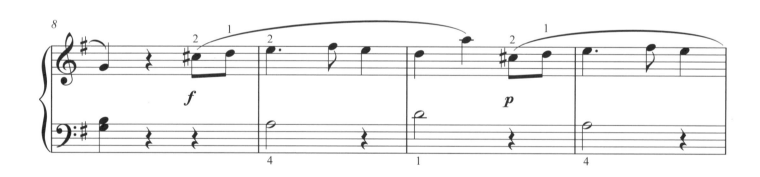

4

March Time

Wilhelm Moritz Vogel
(1846-1922)

Moderato ♩ = 116

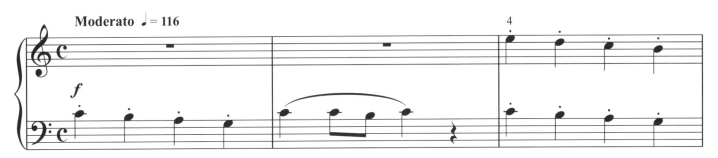

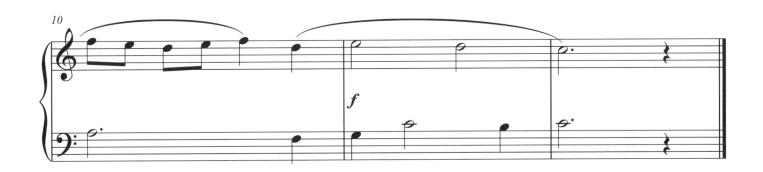

On a Wintry Day

Dulcie Holland
(1913-2000)

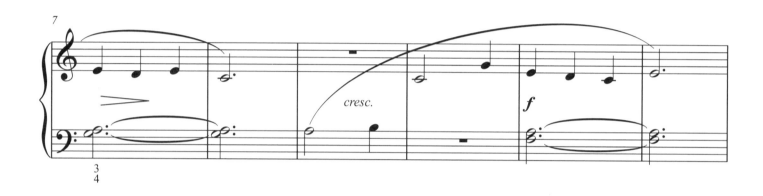

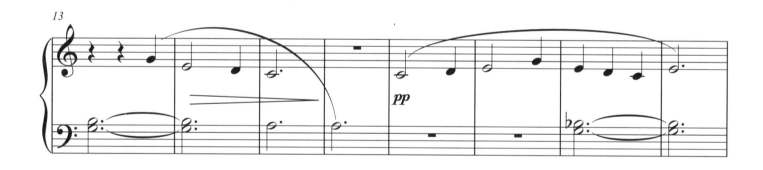

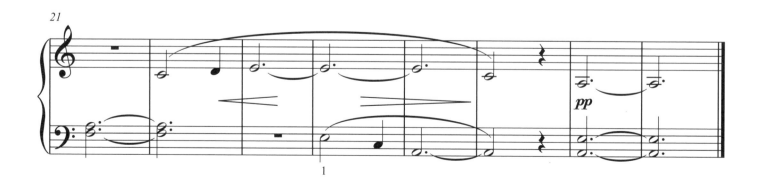

Easy Living

Kay Charlton
(born 1963)

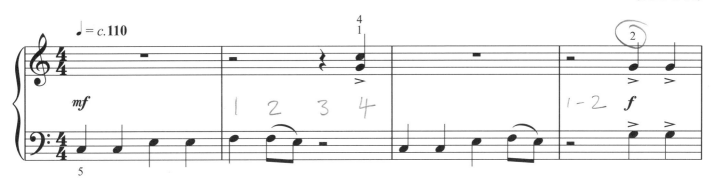

Spring Day

(optional duet part)

Christopher Norton
(born 1945)

Spring Day

(candidate solo part)

Christopher Norton
(born 1945)

The Stroke of Midnight

Sarah Walker
(born 1965)

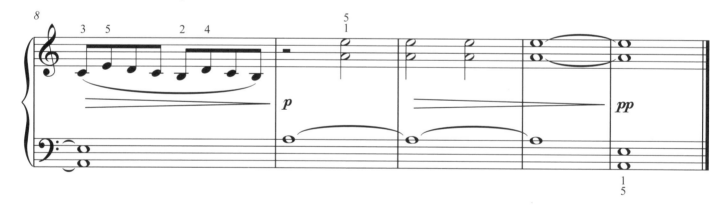

Smooth and Crunchy

Elissa Milne
(born 1967)

Composer's original metronome mark is ♩ = 138

Ready To Go!

Ben Crosland
(born 1968)

Lively, with straight quavers [♩ = 100]

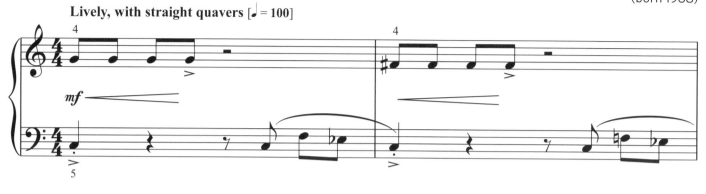

Composer's original metronome mark is ♩ = 104

Exercises

1a. Snow Flakes – tone, balance and voicing

1b. Change of mind – tone, balance and voicing

2a. Sad Moment – co-ordination

2b. Last One In! – co-ordination

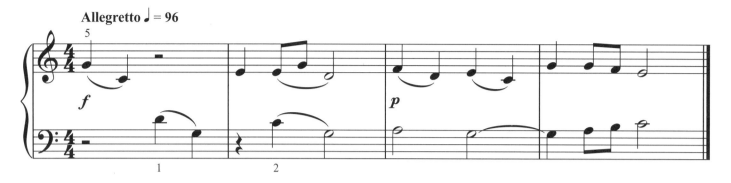

3a. First Frost – finger & wrist strength and flexibility

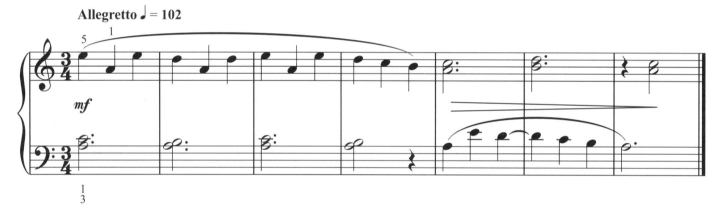

3b. Relay Race – finger & wrist strength and flexibility

Teaching notes

Hook   Gavotte   page 2

True gavottes usually begin on the third beat of a bar and here the main accent comes on the third minim beat of each phrase, so it qualifies as a gavotte, but one written in double time. Words are so useful for teaching phrasing, and here 'I am very *hungry*' should help pianists feel the stress at the beginning of the second bar. The dynamic contrasts and the *crescendo* on the last line should be carefully practised, and take care that the Cs in bars 5 and 13 (treble) do not linger beyond a crotchet. This is standard teaching material and can be played with the duet accompaniment in the exam – helpful for any nervous pianists.

Müller   Summer Swing   page 4

Originally this was titled *Scherzo*, but *Summer Swing* suits its fresh, sunny mood, and the idea of the motion of a swing is useful for achieving those long *legato* lines. The left hand plays a purely accompanimental role, but it is worth spending some time practising the chords in the different dynamics, listening carefully for synchronisation. Fingers should be ready on the notes before playing and be aware of the way the notes go down – faster for the *mf* than for the *p*. The melody should always sing a dynamic notch above the chords, with the wrist helping the hand to lift at the end of the phrases. Watch out for a slightly awkward moment in bar 12, where the melody finishes after a crotchet, while the bass sustains its note for a minim.

Vogel   March Time   page 5

This is a perfectly balanced little march, needing a strong sense of pulse and offering the opportunity to practise *staccato* and *legato* at a variety of dynamic levels. A useful image to help develop this last skill is to think of the marchers getting gradually more distant through bars 5-8, then turning around and returning in full force by the end. The articulation should be crisp in the opening, with the later dotted minims held for exactly three beats and no longer. Interestingly the original title was *The Brave Horseman* and it was marked *pomposo*. Something to keep in mind perhaps to help achieve the upright, unbending pulse.

Holland   On a Wintry Day   page 6

The many minims here may fool you into thinking this is an easy option – it is not! It needs to be played with much sensitivity and tonal control. Try closing your eyes and playing the first three four-bar melodies several times over, listening to an immaculate *legato* between the hands, with a sense of phrasing towards the third bar. Play each phrase in different dynamics, concentrating on listening to the sound and feeling how the notes need to go down more slowly the quieter you want to play. Posture at the piano is always important, but there is a temptation to put the shoulders up and make ourselves physically small when we want to play *piano*. Resist this, and instead feel that you are comfortable and warm inside looking out onto this wintry scene, rather than experiencing its bitter cold.

Charlton   Easy Living   page 7

When you're busy, you long for that day off. Then it comes, and you wonder what to do with all that empty time. There's a similar problem here: the notes are straightforward, with a mix of detached crotchets and pairs of slurred quavers. But the 'easy living' mood gives you lots of free time in the form of rests, and it is important to fill them, to keep that sense of pulse going through them. Obviously counting is one way of doing this, but I also recommend singing in your head some of the music you've just played. So you might imagine another pair of quavers in the crotchet rest in bar 2, or two pairs of quavers for the minim rest in bar 4. You could also try saying words in rhythm: 'this is easy living' will nicely fill the three beats of rests in the penultimate bar. Use a metronome if you must, but it imposes a pulse from the outside, rather than getting musicians to develop one within themselves.

Norton   Spring Day   page 8

Like the previous piece, this has an open, positive atmosphere, largely created by the hands playing in octaves and by the simple primary chord harmonies. Norton has indicated *legato* in bars 2 and 4, so the opening minims should be slightly detached to contrast with this. It may be initially useful to repeat the C on the ties in the second bar as an exercise, just to be completely sure of the syncopated rhythm. This will be especially important when played as a duet. In bars 6 and 8, make a small *diminuendo* in the left hand, being sure to release the right hand C on the second minim. There is a strange clash of harmony in bars 14 and 16 if you play this with a partner. The top part suggests a tonic chord of C, while the *secondo* plays a dominant chord of G. Unusual, but absolutely correct.

Walker   The Stroke of Midnight   page 10

If you count the accented Es and fifths in the bass, then the fifths in the right hand, and finally the very last fifth in the last bar, you will have your 12 chimes of the clock. Midnight: an eerie, slightly scary atmosphere, with an uneasily slow tempo. The bass chimes are always louder and more solid than the frightened *staccato* top part, but in the final bars they disappear to nothing – you will need to start with a healthy *mp* in the right hand in bar 9 to make this possible. I can imagine someone tiptoeing around the house in the darkness, hearing the clock, and then quietly going back to bed and hiding under the covers as the last chimes sound. A simple but brilliantly effective piece.

Milne   Smooth and Crunchy   page 11

The catchy, syncopated nature of this music, alongside the easily learnt notes, will surely make it a favourite choice, even without the peanut butter associations ('with relish', Milne quips). It is, of course, all about *staccato* v *legato*, with some dynamic contrast thrown in for good measure. Practise playing five notes, C–G, hands together, with different articulation in each hand as an exercise. Start really slowly, then gradually build up speed. This is the sort of co-ordination challenge that is supposed to be so good for our brains and, on top of that, the piece is enormous fun to play. Brava Ms Milne!

Crosland   Ready to Go!   page 12

Patting your head while stroking circles on your tummy is a good warm up for this piece, as you're asked to accent the first note in the bass, while making a *crescendo* to the fourth note in the treble. Not easy! Try giving an extra impulse from the arm for the left hand accent, matched in the right hand three quavers later, keeping the wrist flexible so that the sound is buoyant and excited, not hard. You'll want to do the same towards the end – those last two bars are excellent teaching material. An accent on the *staccato* crotchet, two short quavers, then two *tenuto* crotchets (these must be as long as possible without slurring), then a slurred pair of quavers, played with a drop-float technique, and finally two firm accents as you slam the front door and leave.

Barratt   Mopstick Rag   *Chester*

Both hands stay in a G position for this rag, give or take the odd chromatic note, so this will suit pianists who have been using primers such as the Bastien or Alfred series, which cover C and G positions with small chords early on. The dynamics are led by the harmonic movement: the first phrase moves towards the subdominant harmony in the third bar, but the second phrase modulates to the dominant, with a *crescendo* into the new key in bar 8. Let the left hand take us back to *p* for the third phrase, a variation on the first, and then another quicker, more assertive *crescendo* culminates in four final *forte*, detached and accented notes. Keep a feeling of energy in the arms as these are played, avoiding a heavy, hard sound. This rag sounds perfectly good by itself played at pitch, but pianists are welcome to bring a teacher, parent or friend to play the duet part, in which case this page must be played an octave higher. A tempo of around ♩ = 132 works well.

Bullard	A Chat Between Friends	*OUP*

How much more sensible it is to have the thumbs on next door notes, rather than sharing middle C. It gives Bullard an extra note to play with and avoids any awkward choreography. Despite the hands remaining in one position, this piece has much subtlety as the phrasing of each hand overlaps that of the other, just like friends talking together. The small three-note interchanges at the end of the first line will need careful shaping, a *diminuendo* away from the initial note, helped by a gentle lateral wrist movement, followed by a lift on the third note. The subtle contrast between **mp** and **p** demands good listening and exaggerating the difference will probably be a necessary first step. Colours are useful here, a watery powder blue for the first line, then a more luminous turquoise for the second. In the last two bars the friends finally agree and phrase together. Deceptively simple, but actually quite sophisticated. A tempo of 112 is good.

Churchill & Morey		
arr. Sebba	Heigh-ho	*A & C Black*

I wonder if this is as well known by young children today as it was 20 or 30 years ago? It is a wonderfully catchy tune and Jane Sebba has added a jaunty, jazzy walking bass accompaniment that will enhance practice and help to keep the pulse energised but stable. Not to be played in the exam though. A tempo of around 126 is ideal, and also ideal would be to get pianists to sing this first. No phrasing is marked, but there needs to be breathing spaces, probably in bars 4, 7, 10 and 12, although alternatives are possible – look for the commas in the text. Everything else should be played *legato*, unless a rest is marked. The suggested fingering in the left hand between bars 8-9 is counter-intuitive; try putting a 2 on the G in bar 9, followed by a thumb on the next note, middle C. Enjoy!

Hall	Martians' March	*OUP*

This is a straightforward piece with a fun ending. Hall directs us to play it boldly, although the Martians in the picture look a little overawed by their audience of cows and sheep. Get the arm involved to make a good, full sound and ensure the synchronisation of the chords. After two bars of introduction, reduce the volume in the left hand so that the melody can take over our attention. The opening **mf** must allow for the fuller **f** at bar 11, remembering that it is the speed at which the notes go down that will give this extra volume. The final bars are a tease; the *diminuendo* makes the audience think the piece is over then, CRASH! You can use both hands for this final chord: 2 & 3 in one, and 2, 3 & 4 in the other balances the hands well. The whole piece, including the last bar, should have an absolutely unchanging tempo, with a marching speed of ♩ = c.120.

Haughton	Flannagan's Jig	*OUP*

Even were we not given the title, we would surely know this spirited jig comes from Ireland, played on the fiddle or the pub piano! Having the tune alternately in right then left hands is excellent – thank you Mr Haughton – and you could have fun playing it in both at once. You could start both hands on the same note, or play both as written, beginning on D in the treble and G in the bass. Playing scales this way, in two keys at once, can also spice up their practice and is a good co-ordination exercise. Release the accompanying chords rhythmically, probably soon after the middle of the bar and, although there are no articulation marks, it would make sense to aim for a buoyant, but generally smooth touch, with the first crotchets of each two-bar phrase quickly released to allow their repeat. Not too fast, around ♩. = c.100.

Iles	Circle Dance	*OUP*

Start this at a restrained, steady speed, around ♩ = 104. Use a small drop-float movement for the paired quavers, noticing that Iles has stopped the slur before the final crotchet in bar 2, but continued it into the minim in bar 4. Observing small details like this is proof that you've really studied the text, and being able to integrate them into the performance demonstrates good technique. The second line could be where the dancers formally bow to each other and to the bride in the middle of the circle, before they break out into a wild romp on the last line (♩ = c.126). Make sure the minim chords on the second line are long enough; listen through them, maybe hearing an echo of the quavers in your head to make sure that each beat really does last for the same amount of time!

Trad. *arr.* Sebba	Britches Full of Stitches	*A & C Black*

This is a one-trick pony, but no less engaging for that. Play the repeats and make the dynamic contrasts as suggested, with a tempo of around ♩ = 96. Those open fifths in the left hand could be the basis for some improvisation games – 'What shall we do with a drunken sailor?', 'Scarborough Fair' and 'Greensleeves' all come to mind. Keep the dotted rhythm precise and snappy, and practise the small changes of position, checking that the wrist stays flexible.

	Captain Xenon's Intergalactic	
Walker	Mystery Tour	*Faber*

This is a wonderfully imaginative piece and – don't tell anyone – really very easy. It does need the pedal for the piece to work, so probably not for very small children, but it only needs to be depressed and held until the end (when we recorded this, it took about a minute for the sound to completely die away!). This mystery tour is based on the magical sound of the whole tone scale, just six notes of which are played as scales divided between the hands or played in small clusters. A thumb is suggested on the right hand F sharp. Excellent – learning to play black notes with 1 & 5 is essential, but you could play these three black notes with 2, 3 & 4 if you prefer. If your piano hasn't got the very high C notated in bar 8, no matter. The highest note on your instrument, or on the piano in the exam, is all that's needed. Listen for a seamless join between the hands in the scalic bars and note that in bar 5 the articulation wants to be long, albeit slightly detached, but not *staccato*. The suggested tempo is perfect.

Wilton	Little Sonata	*Yorktown Music Press*

All our more contemporary composers are wonderfully imaginative, but it is refreshing to find this simple, balanced, classical piece in the syllabus. Both hands stay in a C position throughout, but this is an opportunity to work on a rounded, comfortable hand position, making sure the little finger plays from the knuckle bridge and doesn't lean on its side, and that the thumb is not too flat and heavy. Listen to the balance between the hands – the bass notes need enough depth of sound to sustain their tone and support the melody, which will sing easily two octaves above. A crotchet speed of around 132 works well.

Teaching notes written by Pamela Lidiard

Key

A solid line denotes a piece within this book.

A dotted line denotes a piece from the alternative list.